Irving, Robert **Electromagnetic Waves** (7-8)
Illustrated by Leonard Everett Fisher. "Brief, clear coverage of
electromagnetics: light, radio, infrared, ultraviolet, X rays, micro-
waves, gamma radiation, and their interrelationships. . . . Well done
and gives an overall view not previously available. Recommended."
LIBRARY JOURNAL. 160 pp. Knopf. (537) 60-5510
A, C*, AS, LJ, HB/

537
Ir8

36971

Irving, Robert

Electro-Magnetic Waves.

Electromagnetic Waves

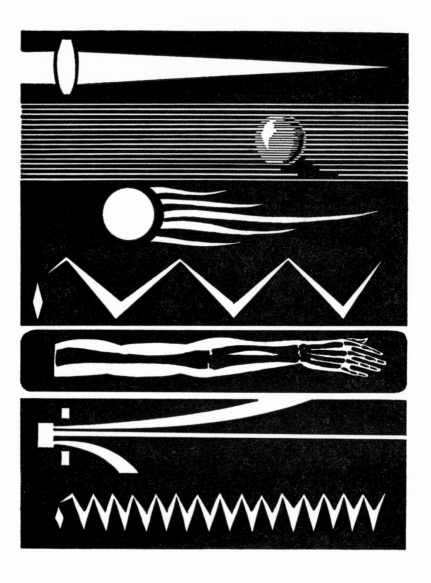

ELECTRO-MAGNETIC WAVES

by ROBERT IRVING

ILLUSTRATED BY LEONARD EVERETT FISHER

1962 : ALFRED A. KNOPF : *NEW YORK*

L. C. CATALOG CARD NUMBER 60–5510

© *Irving Adler, 1960*

THIS IS A BORZOI BOOK,

PUBLISHED BY ALFRED A. KNOPF, INC.

Published April 16, 1960
Second Printing, April 1962

CONTENTS

Electromagnetic Waves

■■■■■■■■■■■■■■■■■■■■■■■■■■■■■■■■■■■■■

1

SEVEN RAYS,
ONE FAMILY

A SMALL WORLD

"Isn't it a small world!" You have probably heard this exclamation many times. People often say it when they find that acquaintances they had met at different times and places, and whom they never connected with each other, turn out to be related to each other. Scientists often have a similar experience with occurrences in nature. Things or events that at first seem to have nothing to do with each other turn out to be related after all. We shall repeat this experience with the seven kinds of rays that are the subjects of this book. We find them in different places, and use them in different ways, but they are close relatives. They are members of one family, the family of *electromagnetic waves.*

SEVEN RAYS

The kind of ray that mankind has known for the longest time is *light.* We meet it every day in sunlight or in lamplight. It helps us see the objects that surround us, when the objects reflect the light into our eyes. Because our eyes can detect light, we call it a *visible* ray. The other rays are *invisible.* We cannot see them, but we can detect them in other ways.

We find three types of invisible rays in use in our homes. When we listen to a radio program we are using the rays that are called *radio waves.* When we cook a meal with an electric broiler, we are using *infrared rays,* sometimes referred to as heat rays. When we sit under a sun-tan lamp, we are using *ultraviolet rays.* We meet the other three types of rays outside the home. At the doctor's office we find *X rays,* produced by X-ray machines, and used for taking pictures of the insides of our bodies. At nearby airports or army posts we find *microwaves,* used with radar equipment to detect planes in the air, or guide them to a safe landing. In hospitals we find *gamma rays* used as invisible bullets to kill cancer cells.

To see why these rays are called electromagnetic waves we have to get acquainted with some facts about magnets and electricity.

THE FIELD AROUND A MAGNET

The ends of a bar magnet are called its *poles.* One is called a north pole, and the other is called a south pole. The poles of two magnets that are held near each other tend to push or pull each other. If the poles are of the same kind (both north or both south), they tend to repel each other or push apart. If they are poles of opposite kinds (one north and one south), they tend to attract each other or pull closer. The strength of the push or pull depends on how far apart the poles are held. The closer the poles are to each other, the stronger is the force with which they push or pull each other. The strength of the force also depends on the strength of the magnets. Some magnets push or pull harder than others. The strength of a pole is measured by comparing its push or pull with that of a standard pole called a *unit pole*. Its pole strength is said to be two, for example, if it pulls twice as hard as a unit pole does.

If a unit north pole is held at some point in the space around a magnet, the push and pull of the poles of the magnet combine to form a single force on it. Such a force exists at every point in the space around the magnet. The collection of all these forces,

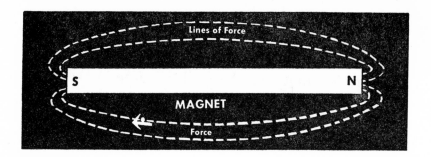

one at each point in space, is called the *magnetic field* around the magnet. The force at each point can be represented by an arrow. The direction of the arrow shows the direction in which a unit pole held at that point is pushed. The length of the arrow shows the strength of the force pushing it. If the unit pole were allowed to move under the action of the force, it would follow a path called a *line of force*. The lines of force around a magnet run from its north pole to its south pole. It is possible to make the lines of force visible with the help of iron filings. Place a piece of paper over a bar magnet, and sprinkle iron filings over the paper. Then tap the paper gently. The iron filings will line up along the lines of force, as shown by the dashes in the drawing on page 7.

There is a magnetic field all the time in the space that surrounds us, because there are many magnets in existence. Each magnet is surrounded by its own magnetic field. If a unit north pole is held at any point in space, each of these magnetic fields exerts a push on it. All these separate pushes add up to form one single force at that point. In this way the separate fields surrounding all the magnets that exist combine to form one field for all of space.

CHANGING THE FIELD

The pole strength of a magnet can be changed. One way of doing it, for example, is to strike the magnet with a hammer. When the pole strength is changed, or if the magnet is moved, a change takes place in the magnetic field in space. The change at each point may be a change in strength of the field force, or a change in its direction, or both. But the change does not take place at all points at the same time. The change occurs first at points right next to the poles of the magnet, and takes place later at points that are further away. The change travels away from the magnet at a definite speed. In empty space, this speed is about 186,000 miles per second.

It may seem strange to talk about a *change* that moves or travels. Our usual experience is with *bodies* that move from one position to another. A change has no body, but its motion can be real anyhow. To see a simple example of how a change can travel, set up a row of dominoes standing on end, one in front of the other. Then knock the first domino down. The result is a change in the position of the domino from

standing up to lying down. This *change* moves down the line as each domino is knocked down in turn by the one in front of it. You can see another example of a traveling change in a line of cars waiting at a traffic light. When the light turns green, the cars start moving, each car changing from rest to motion. But the cars don't all start moving at once. The change from rest to motion moves gradually back from the head of the line at a fairly steady speed.

THE ELECTROSTATIC FIELD

There is another field of force in space that resembles the magnetic field in many ways. It is caused by electrical charges, and is called the *electrostatic field*. Just as there are two kinds of magnetic poles, called north and south, there are two kinds of electrical charges, called positive and negative. Electrical charges can be placed on or removed from a body in various ways. For example, if a glass rod is rubbed with silk, a positive charge is put on the glass. If a hard rubber rod is rubbed with flannel, a negative charge is put on the rubber. These charges are invisible. But they can be detected by their effects. Like charges repel each other, and unlike charges attract each other. If two unlike charges are separated by some distance, lines of force extend across this distance from one charge to the other. A unit positive charge would be pushed along a line of force from the positive charge toward the negative charge. At each point the push on it would have a definite strength and a definite direction. The sum of all such pushes caused by all the electrical charges in the world is the total electrical force at the point.

If an electrical charge is increased or decreased, or if it is moved, a change takes place in the surrounding electrostatic field. Like a change in the magnetic field, it travels out into space at a definite speed. The two types of change are always found traveling out together, because they are closely related.

ELECTRICITY AND MAGNETISM

The connection between electricity and magnetism was found in two important discoveries of the nineteenth century. In 1820 the Danish physicist, Hans Christian Oersted, showed that an electric current is surrounded by a magnetic field. About ten years later, the English physicist, Michael Faraday, and the American physicist, Joseph Henry, showed that a moving or changing magnetic field can pro- duce an electric current in a wire. You can verify

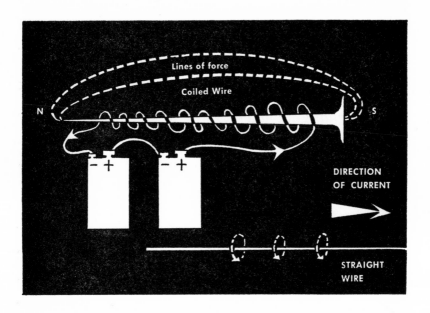

Oersted's discovery for yourself. Wind some No. 18 insulated copper wire around a large soft iron nail, and connect the ends of the wire to a battery of dry cells. You will find that when the current flows through the wire, the nail becomes a magnet capable of picking up small pieces of iron.

An electric current is made up of moving electric charges. When charges move, there is a change in the electrostatic field around them. So the meaning of Oersted's discovery can be expressed in terms of the electrostatic and magnetic fields in space in this way: *A changing electrostatic field produces a magnetic field.* The Faraday-Henry discovery can be described in a similar way: *A changing magnetic field produces an electrostatic field.* This way of describing what happens explains why changes in the electrostatic and magnetic fields travel together. A change in either of the fields always leads to a change in the other. Because the two changes are always linked, the twofold change, as it moves out into space, is called an *electromagnetic* wave.

CHANGES WITH A RHYTHM

If an electric current moves back and forth in a wire, an electromagnetic wave, consisting of changes in the electrical and magnetic fields around the wire, moves off into space. If the current vibrates with a regular rhythm, these changes occur with the same rhythm. The rhythm is called the *frequency* of the wave. For example, the current supplied to you by the electric company has a rhythm of sixty cycles per second. This means that the current in the house wires goes back and forth sixty times in a second. At each point in space there is an electrical force and a magnetic force caused by this current. These forces also vibrate with a frequency of sixty times a second. To see what these vibrations are like, think of each force as an arrow. A cycle of changes, starting from a moment when the arrow has its greatest length, proceeds in this way: The arrow shrinks in length to

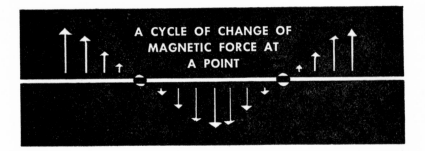

a point. Then the arrow begins growing again, but pointing in the opposite direction. Then it shrinks once more, and after a second reversal of direction grows to its original length. Remember that the length of the arrow represents the strength of the force at the point. The direction of the arrow represents the direction of the force.

For a complete picture of a cycle of changes brought by an electromagnetic wave we need two arrows, one to represent the electrical force at a point, and the other to represent the magnetic force at that point. The two arrows cross each other at right angles, and their vibrations are out of step. One

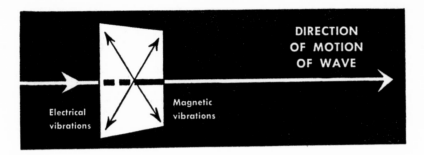

arrow is longest when the other is shortest, and vice versa. The two vibrations take place in a plane, which you can picture as a flat sheet. The plane is at right angles to the direction of motion of the wave that carries these changes from point to point.

A SIMPLIFIED PICTURE

The picture of what happens as an electromagnetic wave moves off into space is complicated by the fact that there are two vibrations taking place at the same time at each point. It is often helpful to simplify the picture by leaving one of these vibrations out. When we consider only one of these vibrations, say the changes in the electrical force, then the wave resembles an ordinary water wave traveling across the surface of a pond. In the diagram below, a water wave is shown moving to the right. The effect

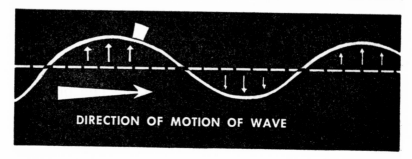

DIRECTION OF MOTION OF WAVE

of the wave on the water may be seen in what happens to a cork floating on the surface. When a crest rolls under the cork, the cork rises. When a trough passes by, the cork falls. So while the wave is moving to the right, the cork is bobbing up and down. Each particle of water on the surface of the pond bobs up and down in the same way. The vertical arrow drawn at each point of the wave shows how far the water is

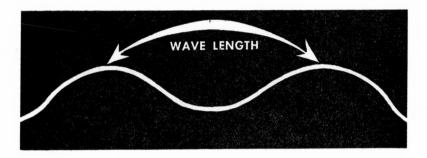

displaced up or down from the middle position when that part of the wave goes by. If we use this picture to represent an electromagnetic wave, then the arrows can represent the electrical force at each point in the path of the wave. As the wave moves to the right, the arrow at a fixed point would grow and shrink up and down.

The distance between two crests that are right next to each other is called the *wavelength* of the wave. It is the distance that the wave moves during the time it takes for one complete cycle of vibration. The frequency, we already know, is the number of cycles in a second. So the frequency times the wavelength equals the distance the wave moves in one second. But this is what we usually call the *speed* of the wave, so we have the important rule for a wave that its *speed equals its frequency times its wavelength*. In the case of a frequency of 60 cycles per second, for example, sixty waves per second times the wavelength must equal 186,000 miles per second. The wavelength then must be (186,000 ÷ 60) miles, or 31,000 miles. Because the product of the frequency and wavelength is a fixed number, a wave with a low frequency has a long wavelength, and vice versa, a wave with a high frequency has a short wavelength.

HOW THE SEVEN RAYS DIFFER

The seven types of rays described in this book all resemble each other in that they are all electromagnetic waves. What makes them different from each other is their frequency or their wavelength. The wavelengths and frequencies of each type are shown in the diagram (on page 22). The wavelengths are expressed in centimeters. One inch is about 2½ centimeters long.

To express some of these wavelengths or frequencies it is necessary to use very large or very small numbers. Scientists find it convenient to express large and small numbers by means of a special shorthand. In this shorthand, to write a large number you first write a number between 1 and 10, and then you show how many times it must be multiplied by 10 to get the large number. For example, to get 3,000,000 you must multiply $3 \times 10 \times 10 \times 10 \times 10 \times 10 \times 10$. In the shorthand, this product is written as 3×10^6, and it is read as "three times ten to the sixth power." To write a small number, you first write a number between 1 and 10, and then show how many times it must be divided by 10 to get the small number. For example, to get .0003, you must divide 3 by 10 four times: $3 \div 10 = .3$; $.3 \div 10 = .03$; $.03 \div 10 = .003$; $.003 \div 10 = .0003$. So, in the shorthand,

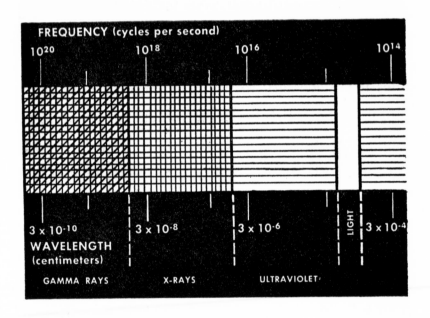

.0003 is written as 3×10^{-4}. The minus sign in front of the four shows that the tens are to be used as divisors instead of multipliers.

Notice that radio waves are the longest of the elec-

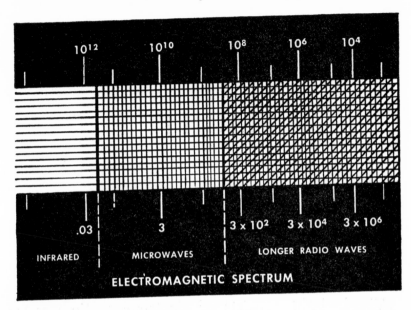

10^{12} 10^{10} 10^8 10^6 10^4

.03   3 3×10^2 3×10^4 3×10^6

INFRARED   MICROWAVES   LONGER RADIO WAVES

ELECTROMAGNETIC SPECTRUM

tromagnetic waves. Because they have the longest waves, they have the lowest frequency. Gamma rays have the shortest waves, and the highest frequency. Visible light is between these two extremes.

2

LIGHT

Visible light consists of electromagnetic waves whose wavelength is between 3.6×10^{-5} centimeters and 7.8×10^{-5} centimeters. The shortest of these waves, 3.6×10^{-5} centimeters, is so small that there are about 60,000 of them to an inch. The longest ones are about twice as long as the shortest, so only about 30,000 of them would fill out an inch.

The frequency of the shortest waves of visible light is about 830 million million cycles per second.

The frequency of the longest waves of visible light is about 390 million million cycles per second.

THE COLORS OF THE RAINBOW

Sometimes, after a late afternoon rain, when the sun is low in the western sky, we see a rainbow arching over the eastern sky. The colors in a rainbow are always arranged in a definite order. One side is red, the other side is violet, and the other colors are arranged between them in this order: red, orange, yellow, green, blue, indigo, violet. Physicists have found that this is actually the order of increasing frequency, or decreasing wavelength. Differences of color are really differences of frequency or wavelength.

Rainbows were a familiar sight for thousands of years. They made people wonder where the colors of the rainbow came from. The mystery was solved by the English physicist Isaac Newton when he showed that the colors are all hidden in the white light of the sun. White light is a mixture of colors. Newton showed that the colors in white light can be sepa-

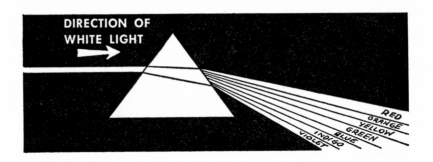

rated by passing a thin beam of light through a glass prism. The prism bends the path of the light as it passes through, but it bends each color by a different amount. So while the colors enter the glass along the same path, they leave it by slightly different paths. As a result, the colors emerge spread out side by side instead of mixed together. A rainbow is formed in the same way. After a rain, there are small water droplets hanging in the air. Light from the sun is reflected to our eyes by the droplets. The droplets behave like little prisms. They bend the colored rays and separate them to form the rainbow.

When a mixture of waves of different frequencies is separated so that the different frequencies appear side by side, the result is called a *spectrum*. The rainbow is one example of a spectrum of visible light. You can sometimes see another example of it in your bathroom, when a narrow beam of sunlight, coming past a window shade, strikes the beveled edge of the bathroom mirror. The edge acts like a prism and separates the colors as it reflects them, to form a spectrum on the wall or floor of the room.

A FAMOUS ARGUMENT

During the seventeenth century scientists offered two different theories on the nature of light. Isaac Newton favored the theory that a beam of light was a stream of small particles or corpuscles. This theory would account for the fact that light travels in straight lines. However, scientists were aware of the fact that the path of a light beam was not always exactly straight. Shadows cast by a body standing in the light were slightly fuzzy at the edge, as if the light were able to turn around a corner the way a water wave does. So the Dutch scientist, Christian Huyghens, concluded that light must be a form of wave motion, resulting from vibrations in space. For a long time, most scientists accepted Newton's theory. But in 1801, the English scientist Thomas Young made a discovery that revived the wave theory of light. He found that it is possible to produce darkness by mixing two beams of light. This fact could not be explained by Newton's theory that light was made up of particles. In Young's experiment, a beam of light was split by shining it on two slits that were close to each other in a screen. On the other side of

YOUNG'S
INTERFERENCE
EXPERIMENT

the screen, the two beams that came from the slits fell on the wall. There, instead of just making a patch of light, they formed a pattern, called an *interference pattern,* of thin bands of light separated by bands of darkness. This pattern is easily explained by the wave theory of light. The bands of light are places where the waves in the two beams arrive in step. There a crest comes together with a crest and a trough with a trough. The vibrations of both waves are in the same direction and they strengthen each other, producing a brighter light. The bands of darkness are places where the waves in the two beams arrive out of step. There a crest of one wave comes together with a trough of the other. The vibrations of the two waves are in opposite directions, and they cancel each other, producing darkness. Young's experiment even provided a way of measuring the wavelength of the light in the beam. The wavelength could be calculated from the distance between the slits and the distance between the dark lines in the interference pattern.

After Young's experiment, scientists became fully convinced that light was a form of wave motion. They lost interest in Newton's corpuscular theory and let it die. But they had to revive it again in 1900 to account for some newly discovered facts. In Germany, Max Planck, studying heat radiation, and Albert Einstein, studying the way light may knock electrons out of a metal, found that a light beam is made up of a stream of small particles. These particles are called *photons*. Now, after over 250 years of the argument about the nature of light, we see that both sides of the argument were right. Light is a wave, but it is made up of corpuscles.

THE ENERGY OF A PHOTON

The two theories are united in an interesting way in the modern picture of the photon. The corpuscular theory is used when we describe the photon as a small particle, a little bundle of energy. But we need the wave theory to measure the energy in the bundle. It turns out that the amount of energy in a photon depends on the frequency of the wave that carries it. The higher the frequency, the higher the energy of the photon. A photon of violet light has more energy than a photon of red light.

CONCENTRATING LIGHT

If two prisms are placed base to base, as shown in the drawing, they can be used for concentrating a

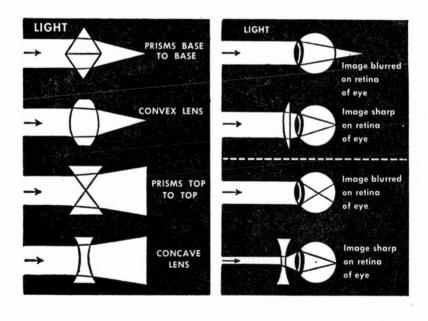

beam of light. The upper prism bends the light down, and the lower prism bends the light up. As a result, the double prism squeezes a wide beam of light into a narrow space. A convex lens is like a double prism and has the same effect. If two prisms are placed with their narrow parts together, as shown in the drawing, then they make the light fan out. A concave lens has this effect, too.

When light enters the human eye it first passes through a lens which serves to focus the light on a sensitive screen in the eye called the retina. In the eye of some people the lens doesn't bend the light enough to bring it to a sharp focus on the retina. Such people use convex lenses in their eyeglasses to help the lenses in their eyes bend the light. In the eyes of others, their natural lenses bend the light too much. These people use concave lenses in their eyeglasses to make the light fan out a bit before it enters their eyes.

It is also possible to concentrate light with the help of a curved mirror. If a beam of light strikes a parabolic mirror, as shown in the drawing, each part of

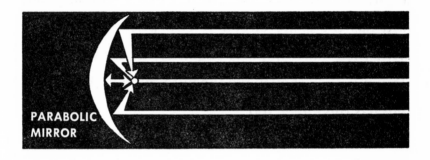

PARABOLIC
MIRROR

the mirror reflects the light in a different direction. The reflected rays all come together at a point called the focus of the mirror. Astronomers use mirrors like this in their telescopes to concentrate starlight. The same kind of mirror can be used in reverse. Light coming from the focus is reflected away from the mirror in a straight beam. Curved mirrors are used this way as reflectors in searchlights.

BENDING LIGHT WITH SCRATCHES

If a glass plate is covered with a thin layer of metal, and parallel scratches are made through the layer, the scratches behave like the slits in Young's screen. When light is passed through the scratches, an interference pattern is formed. The light emerges on the other side of the glass in several distinct beams separated by dark spaces. The beams leave the glass at different angles as if the light had been bent on the way through. Beams of different colors are bent through different amounts, some colors being bent more than others, so the scratches have the same effect as a prism. They separate the colors of a mixture of light, and spread them out in a spectrum. A scratched plate used in this way is called a *diffraction grating*. A typical grating may have as many as 14,-000 scratches per inch. Uses of the spectrum made by a grating are discussed in later chapters.

A long playing phonograph record, like a grating, has a lot of scratches or grooves crowded into a small space. For this reason, when the record reflects light, it behaves the way a grating does. It spreads the light out into a spectrum. To see the spectrum, hold a phonograph record in the light, and tilt it so that the reflected light strikes your eyes. You will see flashes of color on the record, arranged like the colors of a rainbow.

TRANSMITTER FOR LIGHT

Radio waves are sent out into space by transmitters at a broadcasting station. Light waves are also sent out by transmitters. The transmitters for light are atoms, the tiny particles of which all material bodies are built. According to the modern theory of the atom, each atom consists of a core called the *nucleus,* surrounded by electrons that revolve around

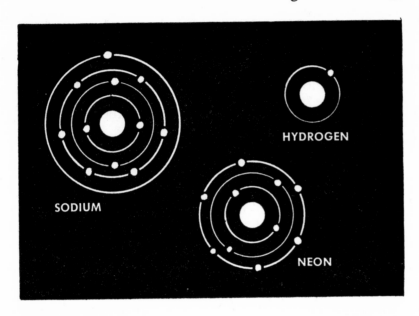

it the way the planets revolve around the sun. Inside the nucleus there are protons, which have a positive electrical charge, and neutrons which have no charge. The electrons have a negative electrical charge. The electrons are held in their orbits by the pull of the positive charge in the nucleus. Each whirling electron is like a vibrating electric current. But it doesn't send out waves while it is vibrating in its orbit. It broadcasts light only when it changes from one orbit to another. Each orbit is like a step on which the electron may stay. While it is on the step, the electron has hidden within it a fixed amount of energy, so the steps are described as energy levels. If an electron is struck by a moving particle, it can be pushed to a higher level. Pushing it to a higher level gives the electron an extra amount of energy. When it falls back to its old level again, the electron gives up this extra energy as a photon of light.

The electrons around a nucleus are arranged about it in layers or *shells.* The electrons in the outermost shell are held most loosely around the nucleus, so they are the ones that are most easily pushed to a higher level. These outer electrons are chiefly responsible for the light coming from glowing bodies. When electrons send out light, the color of the light depends on how much energy is in the photons that are released. It takes more energy to make a photon of violet light than to make a photon of red light, because violet light has a higher frequency than red light.

RECEIVERS FOR LIGHT

We use a radio to receive radio waves. We use special receivers, too, for light waves. Some of these receivers, as our eyes, we get from nature. Other receivers, as the camera, were invented by man. When light enters the eye, it is focussed by the lens of the eye on the *retina* that covers the back wall of the eye. The light causes chemical and electrical changes in the retina. These changes cause signals to be sent to the brain through the optical nerve.

A camera is an imitation eye. In place of the retina, it uses an emulsion spread out over a film. This emulsion contains a compound of silver. To take a picture of an object, we allow light that comes from the object to enter the camera. The lens of the camera focusses the light on the emulsion, to form a picture over it. Wherever light strikes the emulsion, a change takes place within it. This change transfers the picture to the emulsion. To make the picture visible, we have to "develop" the film. This is done by placing it in a chemical bath. The chemical action releases black particles of silver in the changed parts of the emulsion. Then the film is placed in another chemical bath to wash out the unchanged parts of the emulsion. The black particles of silver in the film make up a reverse picture or "negative." It is dark where the object photographed was light, and it is light where the object photographed was dark.

POLARIZED LIGHT

The vibrations of a light wave are at right angles to the direction in which the wave is traveling. To get a rough picture of these vibrations in a narrow beam that is traveling in a straight line, compare the direction of the beam to the axle of a wheel. Directions at right angles to the axle lie across it like the spokes of the wheel. As the diagram below shows, there are

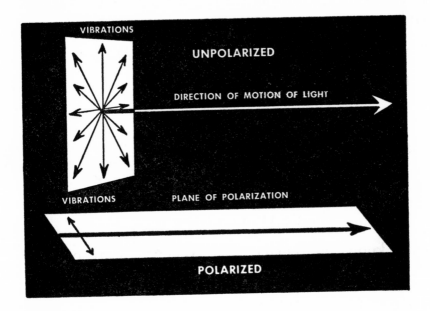

many such directions. In a beam of light coming from the sun, there are vibrations in all these directions, because the beam is a mixture of photons coming from millions of atoms vibrating in many ways. We call this kind of light *unpolarized* light. Light in which the vibrations take place in only one direction is called *polarized light.* In polarized light, the vibrations of the light wave are all within a single flat surface or plane that contains the path of the light and the direction of the vibrations. This plane is called the *plane of polarization.*

SEEING DOUBLE

There are some materials that convert unpolarized light into polarized light. One of them is a rock crystal known as Iceland spar. When a beam of light passes through Iceland spar, it is split into two beams, each of which is bent in a different direction. Both beams are polarized, and their planes of polarization are at right angles to each other. If you look at an object through a crystal of Iceland spar, your eye receives light from two different directions, so you see the object double.

If two pieces of Iceland spar are cut properly and cemented together, the cemented crystal will transmit only one of the split beams while it reflects the other. The crystal behaves as if it has a long slit in it that allows only vibrations that are parallel to the slit to pass through. There are many other materials that have the property of polarizing light that passes through them. Some, like Polaroid, are made of small particles suspended in a sheet of transparent plastic. The particles allow vibrations in only one direction to pass through. Ordinary glass also polarizes light. When a beam of light strikes the surface of a flat sheet of glass, part of the light is reflected, and part of it passes through the glass. Both the reflected and the transmitted beam are polarized.

REMOVING GLARE

If unpolarized light enters a sheet of Polaroid, it comes out polarized. If polarized light enters the Polaroid sheet, it may be blocked altogether. The vibrations in the polarized light are all within its plane of polarization. The Polaroid sheet behaves as if it has a slit in it, and allows only vibrations that are parallel to the slit to pass through. If the sheet is turned so that the "slit" is at right angles to the plane of polarization of the light, then the light is blocked. This property of Polaroid sheets is used in fliers' goggles to remove windshield glare. The glare is made up of polarized light. The flier moves a small lever on his goggles to turn the Polaroid lenses in them until they are in the right position to block this polarized light.

GUIDING LIGHT OF BEES

Daylight comes from all parts of the daytime sky. It consists of sunlight that has been scattered by the molecules of air above us. The scattering takes place in this way: The photons in the light coming from the sun collide with molecules in their path. Each such collision sets a molecule vibrating at right angles to the path of the light. Then the vibrating molecule sends out light itself. In each part of the sky, there are many vibrating molecules, vibrating in all possible directions across the line that joins them to the sun, like the spokes of a wheel across its axle. When we look at molecules that lie between us and the sun, we see all these vibrations, so the light we see is unpolarized. When we look at a part of the sky that is off at an angle from the sun, we see only some of these vibrations in full strength, as shown in the diagram below. As a result, the light we see is partly or completely polarized. The amount of the polarization depends on the direction in which we look and the position of the sun in the sky.

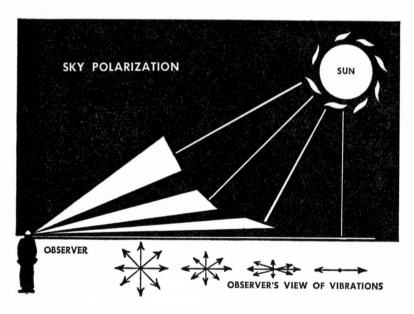

Recently scientists found that the polarized light from the sky plays a part in the flight of insects. A bee, for example, is guided in its flight by the amount of polarization of the light that comes from the direction in which the bee faces.

TURNING A COMET'S TAIL

When a photon of light strikes a molecule, it gives it a push. A beam of light shining on a cloud of molecules tends to push it in the direction in which the beam is traveling. This push is known as *radiation pressure*. Radiation pressure is responsible for the tail of a comet. A comet is a swarm of small particles

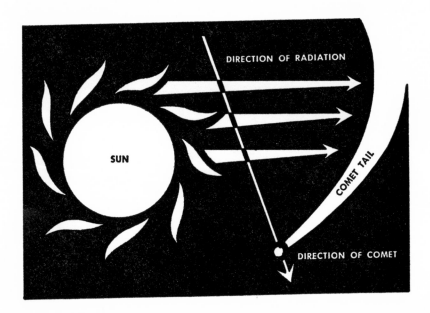

moving in a long narrow orbit around the sun. When it passes close to the sun it is partly evaporated, and then the radiation pressure of the sun's rays pushes the vapor away to form the comet's tail. The tail trails away from the sun, like the smoke of a locomotive blown by the wind.

3

INFRARED RAYS

INVISIBLE HEAT RAYS

In 1800, the German-born British astronomer, Sir
William Herschel, passed a beam of sunlight through
a prism to spread it out in a spectrum. Then he held
a thermometer in different parts of the spectrum to
measure the heating effect of light of different colors.
He moved the thermometer out past the red end of
the spectrum, into a space where there was no light
visible at all. To his surprise, the mercury rose higher
there than it did in the colored light. This was the

first discovery that there are invisible heat rays in sunlight. They are called infrared rays because they are beyond the red end of the visible spectrum. Their position beyond the red shows that they have longer waves and a lower frequency than red light. Today infrared rays are divided into three groups. The near infrared consists of waves whose frequency is below that of red light, 390 million million cycles per second, but is above 200 million million cycles per second. The middle infrared group extends beyond that to about 50 million million cycles per second. The far infrared group reaches to 1 million million cycles per second. At this end of the infrared spectrum a single wave is three hundredths of a centimeter long. This is about four hundred times as long as a single wave of red light.

INFRARED TRANSMITTERS

Every material body is made of atoms and groups of atoms called molecules. When atoms and molecules vibrate, they broadcast infrared rays into space. Since the atoms and molecules of every body do vibrate, every body is a transmitter for infrared rays. The amount of vibration and the amount of radiation depend on how hot the body is. The hotter a body is, the more radiation it sends out. The radiation is spread out among many wavelengths. The share of the total radiation that is found in each wavelength depends on the temperature of the body.

INFRARED RECEIVERS

Every body is also an infrared receiver. When infrared rays fall on the body, they make its atoms and molecules vibrate more, and the body grows warmer. Some bodies are better receivers than others. The best receivers for infrared rays are *black* bodies. They absorb the rays that strike them and turn them into heat. Bodies that are not black absorb only part of the rays and reflect or transmit the rest.

HEAT LAMPS

In an electric broiler, enough electric current flows through a coil of wire to make it red hot. The hot coil sends out a small amount of red light and a larger amount of invisible infrared light. The infrared light does most of the work of cooking the food we place under the coil.

There are some illnesses that doctors treat by applying heat to the body. They use special heat lamps that make infrared light and focus it at the spot where it is needed.

SEEING THROUGH A HAZE

Our eyes cannot see infrared light, but a camera can. There are special films that are sensitive to infrared light, so they can take pictures with this kind of invisible light. A camera equipped with film that is sensitive to infrared light can take a picture right through a haze. A haze is caused by dust particles hanging in the air. Visible light traveling through hazy air is scattered by the dust particles. If the haze is thick, the light never gets through. That's why we cannot see what is behind a thick haze. But infrared rays are not affected by a haze. Their waves are so long that they pass right by and around the dust particles without being scattered. So, while haze is like a screen that blocks visible light, it doesn't block infrared light. The infrared light comes right through. That is why a camera with infrared film can see through a haze.

TAKING PICTURES IN DARKNESS

Infrared rays can also be used to take a picture of something in total darkness. Suppose, for example, an airplane is flying over a city that has been blacked out. Every building in the city, because of its heat, is sending out infrared rays. The plane can take a picture of the city by means of these rays, if it is equipped with a far infrared camera. In the far infrared camera, the rays fall on a sensitive instrument that converts heat into an electric current. The current is used to produce a light whose brightness varies as the strength of the infrared rays varies. The light is directed onto a photographic film to produce a picture. The camera sweeps across the city in a series of lines the way our eyes sweep across a page of a book when we read. The light sweeps across the film in a series of lines in the same way, so the final picture is made up of lines one under the other.

HOW HOT IS A STAR?

There are infrared rays in the light that comes to us from the sun, a star, or a planet. If the light is spread out in a spectrum, it is possible to measure what share of the light is found in each wavelength. Since these shares depend on how hot the radiating body is, this is a way of measuring the temperature of the body. Measurements made in this way show that the temperature on the surface of the sun is about ten thousand degrees Fahrenheit. The temperature of the bright star Sirius is about 19,000 degrees Fahrenheit. The bright side of the planet Venus has a temperature of about 110 degrees Fahrenheit.

FINGERPRINTING A CHEMICAL

You can identify a person by his fingerprints. There is also a way of identifying a chemical by taking its "fingerprints." Every chemical is made up of special clusters of atoms. Each cluster of atoms has its own way of vibrating. Because of the way it vibrates, it radiates some wavelengths of infrared strongly, while it radiates other wavelengths hardly at all. Every chemical can also absorb infrared light, and it absorbs best those wavelengths that it radiates

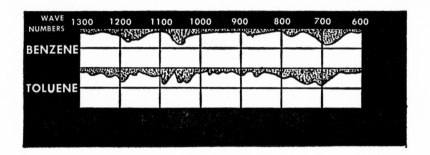

best. If a chemical is dissolved in a liquid, and infrared light is passed through it, the chemical will
absorb some wavelengths, and allow others to pass
through undisturbed. It is as though the chemical
put its fingerprints on the light. If the transmitted
light is spread out in a spectrum, it is possible to
measure how much light of each wavelength came
through. This information is plotted as a curve on
graph paper. Each small section of the curve represents a definite wavelength, and the strength of
each wavelength that came through is shown by the

height of that section of the curve. The nature of
the chemical can be recognized from the shape of the
curve.

4

ULTRAVIOLET RAYS

BEYOND THE VIOLET

When sunlight is spread out in a spectrum, the colors in it are separated and arranged side by side in order of increasing frequency from red to violet. But these visible colors make up only part of the spectrum. We have already seen that there is an invisible part of the spectrum beyond its red end, made up of lower frequency infrared rays. There is another invisible section of the spectrum beyond the violet end, made up of waves that have a higher frequency than violet light. Because they are located just beyond the violet end of the visible spectrum, we call these waves ultraviolet rays. They were first discovered by Johann Wilhelm Ritter, a German scientist, in 1801. They range in frequency from about 830 million million cycles a second to about 75,000 million million cycles per second.

ULTRAVIOLET TRANSMITTERS

Ultraviolet light is broadcast by atoms in the same way that visible light is. It is sent out by an electron in the outer shell of an atom when the electron falls from a high energy level to a lower one. The amount of energy an electron loses between levels is equal to the amount of energy in the photon it sends out, and the frequency of the photon depends on this amount of energy. So whether the photon consists of visible light or ultraviolet light depends on how large a drop of energy the electron falls through. The smaller drops lead to flashes of visible light. The larger drops lead to flashes of ultraviolet light.

A common lamp that produces ultraviolet light is the mercury vapor lamp. The mercury atoms sealed in the lamp are bombarded by a stream of fast-moving electrons. There are many collisions between the moving electrons and those that are in orbits within the mercury atoms. The collisions push these orbital electrons up to higher energy levels. When they fall back to the lower levels again they radiate both ultraviolet light and visible light.

ULTRAVIOLET RECEIVERS

Ultraviolet light affects a photographic film in the same way that visible light does. So photographic film can serve as a detector for ultraviolet light.

Another type of receiver for ultraviolet light is an

ionization chamber. An ionization chamber is a gas-filled tube that has an electrical voltage or pressure applied between two terminals in the tube. The gas is not a conductor of electricity, so a current does not flow between the terminals. The voltage puts a strain on the atoms of the gas, so that their outer electrons are almost torn away from them. If a photon of ultraviolet light enters the chamber, it collides with some of the atoms and tears these loosely held electrons away. This opens up a pathway through which an electric current can flow through the tube, and a surge of current flows between the terminals. The more photons that enter the tube, the more surges of current take place. So an ionization chamber placed in the path of a beam of ultraviolet light can measure the strength of the beam.

Human skin is an ultraviolet ray receiver, too. It responds to ultraviolet light by turning red or tan. Sunburn is caused by the ultraviolet light in sunlight. A sun lamp, which can give you an indoor tan (or a burn, if you use it carelessly) is simply a lamp that produces ultraviolet rays.

SEEING THE INVISIBLE

Most of the electromagnetic waves that are invisible cannot be seen with our eyes because the retina is not sensitive to them. Ultraviolet rays are invisible for another reason. The retina *is* sensitive to them, but they normally never reach the retina. When light enters the eye, it passes through the lens first. But the lens acts like a filter, and removes the ultraviolet rays that may be in the light. If the natural lens of the eye were removed and replaced by a clear glass lens, the eye would be able to see by ultraviolet light. This has actually happened to some people whose lenses had to be removed in an operation for cataract (a film that grows across the eye and blocks the

3 6 9 7 (

light). Their eyes, equipped with glass lenses, can see clearly in ultraviolet light where the normal eye sees only total darkness.

FLUORESCENCE

There are some materials that can convert ultraviolet light into visible light. When ultraviolet light falls on such a material, it begins to glow, often in brilliant colors. This kind of glow is called *fluorescence*. It is caused in this way: A photon of ultraviolet strikes an atom of the fluorescent material and kicks one of its electrons up to a higher energy level. The energy that the photon passes on to the electron is partly converted into heat, so when the electron falls, it releases less energy than it received. The smaller amount of energy goes off as a photon with a lower frequency than that of the photon that hit the electron in the first place. In fact, the frequency is

low enough for the photon to be in the visible range. A material that glows under ultraviolet light (often called u.v. light, for short), is known as a *phosphor*. If the glow persists even after the u.v. light is turned off, it is called *phosphorescence*.

We use the glow of a phosphor as a source of light in *fluorescent lamps*. A fluorescent lamp is a long cylindrical glass tube with a phosphor painted on the inside surface of the tube, and with a gas enclosed in the tube. When an electric current flows through the gas, it makes the gas give out ultraviolet light. The ultraviolet light strikes the phosphor, and makes it glow with visible light.

TWO PICTURES IN ONE

There are some fluorescent dyes that have one color when seen by ordinary light, but glow with a totally different color if the light is turned off and u.v. light is shined on them instead. Costumes that are colored with such dyes are used to produce startling effects on the stage. By changing from an ordinary spotlight to a u.v. spotlight, the costume can be made to change color. If dyes like these are used as paint pigments, it is possible to make hidden pictures that are invisible in ordinary light, but can be seen in u.v. light. This has been done in some advertising billboards to make two pictures in one. Two lamps are turned on the billboard, one bathing it with ordinary light, while the other pours out u.v. light. The lamps are turned on alternately, so that while one lamp is on, the other one is off. When the ordinary lamp is on, one of the pictures on the billboard is seen. When the u.v. lamp is on, that picture vanishes, and the hidden one, glowing now with fluorescent light, takes its place.

GERM KILLER

When a photon strikes a molecule, it gives it a push. How hard the push is depends on how much energy the photon carries. The energy, in turn, depends on the frequency of the wave of the photon. When a photon of infrared light strikes a molecule, it pushes it gently and enables it to vibrate. The vibration of many molecules is heat, so the chief effect of infrared light is to warm up any body that it strikes. Ultraviolet light has a much higher frequency than infrared light. So a photon of ultraviolet light carries more energy than a photon of infrared light does. As a result it doesn't push so gently. A photon of ultraviolet light is like a speeding bullet. When it strikes a molecule, it hits it so hard that it may break it. If many u.v. photons strike molecules inside a living cell, they may break enough of them to upset the delicate chemical balance in the cell and kill it. For this reason, ultraviolet light is capable of killing bacteria. The use of u.v. light as a germ killer was first developed systematically by the Danish physician, Niels R. Finsen. Dr. Finsen designed a special u.v. lamp, known as Finsen's light, which he used for curing certain skin diseases. For introducing new and valuable methods of treatment, Dr. Finsen was awarded the Nobel prize for medicine in 1903.

DEATH RAYS IN SUNLIGHT

A large animal like a human being is made up of many living cells. Ultraviolet light can kill these cells, too. A small amount of ultraviolet light will kill only a few cells in the skin, so it doesn't do much harm. At the same time, the u.v. light helps the skin produce Vitamin D, a chemical that the body needs for good health. So the small amount of u.v. light we usually receive in sunlight does the human body more good than harm. But a large amount of u.v. light can kill a large number of cells and cause a bad burn. Many people are reminded of this fact very painfully each summer when they expose themselves to too much sunshine at the beach. Fortunately, the human body has a way of protecting itself against ultraviolet light. When bombarded with u.v. light, the skin cells produce dark particles that serve as a shield for the cells. These dark particles give the skin a tan color. The more sun tan you have, the more sunshine you can receive without getting a burn. If you build up a tan gradually, by exposing yourself to the sun for only a few minutes at a time at first, you can take larger doses of sunshine later without getting a burn.

When sunlight enters the earth's atmosphere, it contains much more u.v. light than we ever find in the sunshine at the ground. In fact there is enough u.v. light in it to make sunshine a death ray capable of killing every living thing that it strikes. However, most of this deadly u.v. light is removed from the sunshine by the air. One-fifth of the air is made up of oxygen. High up in the air, about fifteen miles above the ground, most of the u.v. photons are stopped by collisions with molecules of oxygen. These collisions cause a reshuffling of the atoms of oxygen. They break up molecules of ordinary oxygen, which have two atoms of oxygen in every molecule, and recombine the atoms to form *ozone,* which has three atoms of oxygen in each molecule. The layer of air where this action takes place is called the *ozone layer.* The ozone layer soaks up most of the u.v. rays in the sunlight, so they never reach the ground. In this way it serves as a shield that protects us.

5

RADIO WAVES

THE DISCOVERY OF RADIO WAVES

We know that radio waves exist. We get daily proof of this fact when we turn on a radio or television set to listen to our favorite programs. We also know that radio waves and light waves are related to each other as members of the family of electromagnetic waves. Both of these facts were unknown about one hundred years ago. They were discovered chiefly through the work of two scientists, the Englishman

James Clerk Maxwell, and the German Heinrich
Hertz.

The first step towards the discovery of radio waves
was taken by Maxwell. He had gathered together the
known facts about electricity and magnetism and
set out to summarize them in a convenient way. His
summary took the form of a set of equations first
published in 1862, and now known as the Maxwell
equations. Studying his own equations, he found
hidden in them an unsuspected fact. The equations
predicted that when an electric current is made to
vibrate back and forth in a wire, it would send out
an electromagnetic wave. The equations also predicted what the speed of this wave would be. They
forecast that the speed would be 186,000 miles per
second, exactly the same as the speed of light. It was
unlikely that the agreement of the two speeds could
be a mere coincidence. Maxwell decided that radio
and light waves had the same speed because they

were waves of the same kind, differing only in frequency and wave length. He proposed the electromagnetic theory of light, which pictures light as an electrical and magnetic disturbance in space.

Heinrich Hertz took the next step in 1886 by proving that Maxwell's theory was right. Guided by the theory, he designed apparatus for producing and receiving radio waves. His transmitter, placed at one end of his laboratory, was a spark coil that forced a rapidly alternating current across a small gap in a brass rod. His receiver was a similar rod at the other end of the room. When he turned on his transmitter, he could see sparks jump across the gap in the receiver. Radio waves, as Maxwell had predicted, were traveling across the room and causing a current to vibrate in the receiver in step with the vibrations in the transmitter. In a series of carefully planned experiments, Hertz measured the wavelength, the frequency, and the speed of the waves. As Maxwell had predicted, the speed was the same as the speed of light. Hertz also showed that radio waves could be bent by lenses and reflected by mirrors the way light waves are.

LONG WAVES

Radio waves are the longest members of the family of electromagnetic waves. In the spectrum, in which the waves are arranged in order of increasing wavelength, they lie beyond the infrared waves. Their wavelengths range from about three hundredths of a centimeter (the longest infrared waves) to about 300 kilometers (185 miles). The waves that Hertz produced were about two feet long. Today they would be classified as *microwaves*, because they are in the short wave section of the radio wave spectrum. Radio and television broadcasts use longer waves. Although microwaves were the first radio

waves to be produced, it is interesting that they were
the last ones to be put to a practical use. Because
the long waves and microwaves are produced by
different methods and are used in different ways, we
shall discuss them separately. This chapter deals
with the long waves, whose wavelength is ten feet
or more. Chapter VIII deals with microwaves, whose
wavelength is less than ten feet, but more than three
hundredths of a centimeter.

Radio broadcasts today are made by two different
methods, known as AM and FM. The frequencies of
the waves used are expressed in kilocycles or megacycles. One kilocycle is one thousand cycles per second. One megacycle is one million cycles per second.
AM radio stations use frequencies from 535 kilocycles (with a wavelength of about 600 meters) to
1,605 kilocycles (with a wavelength of about 200
meters). FM radio stations use frequencies from 88.1
megacycles (with a wavelength of about three and

a half meters) to 107.9 megacycles (with a wavelength of about three meters).

THE TANK CIRCUIT

Radio waves are produced by a vibrating electrical current in a radio transmitter. The frequency of the vibrations is controlled by a part of the transmitter known as a *tank circuit*. To understand the job of the tank circuit, let us first look at a more familiar kind of vibration that is not electrical, that of a pendulum, made of a weight hanging from a string. If the weight is pulled aside and then released, the pendulum begins to swing back and forth with a regular frequency. Every pendulum has its own natural frequency. The frequency depends on the length of the string. The longer the string is, the lower the frequency is. So we can control the frequency of the pendulum by adjusting the length of the string. A

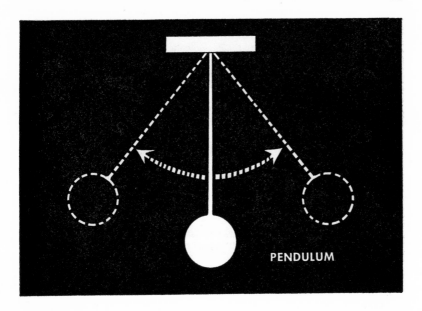

PENDULUM

tank circuit also has a natural frequency. Just as the frequency of the vibrations of a pendulum depends on its length, the frequency of the vibrations in a tank circuit depends on two quantities called *inductance* and *capacitance*. The inductance is supplied mostly by a coil, which has a tendency to resist changes in the electric current. When the current starts, the coil tends to stop it. When the current

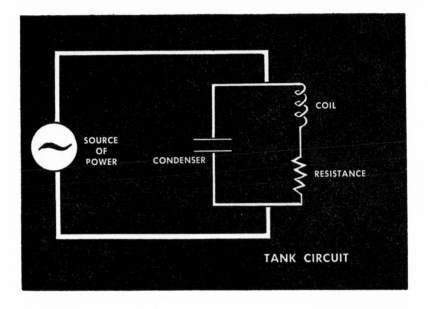

stops, the coil tends to keep it going. The inductance of the coil depends on its size and shape and the number of turns of wire in it. The capacitance is supplied mostly by a condenser, which acts like a storage tank for electrical charge. If the condenser is made of two metal plates separated by a gap, its capacitance depends on the size of the plates, the width of the gap, and the kind of material that is in the gap. We can control the frequency of the electrical vibrations in a tank circuit by adjusting the coil to the right amount of inductance and the condenser to the right amount of capacitance.

BUILDING UP THE VIBRATIONS

There is a third quality in any electrical circuit known as its *resistance*. The resistance converts part of the electrical energy into heat. The result of this loss of electrical energy is a steady weakening of any current flowing through the circuit. If electrical vibrations are started in a tank circuit, the resistance makes them die out, unless something is done to strengthen them again and again. This is done by giving the current a series of rhythmic pushes that are in step with the vibrations. The chief device for boosting the vibrations in this way is the radio tube. Here is how it may be done, for example, by the simplest type of "three electrode" tube. The electrodes, known as cathode, plate, and grid, are sealed into a tube from which all air has been removed. One type of cathode is a wire through which an

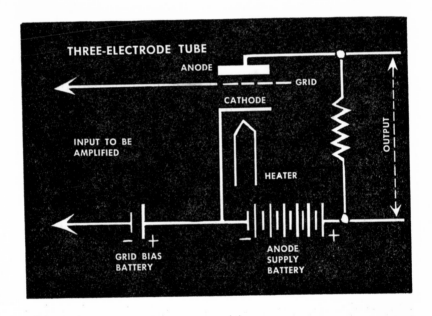

electric current flows. The wire becomes hot, and electrons leak off the wire into the empty space around it. Outside the tube, the plate is joined to the cathode through a power source in such a way that a positive charge is placed on the plate. The positive charge pulls on the electrons that come off the cathode, so a current flows from the cathode to the plate. This is known as the plate current. The grid is a wire mesh placed between the cathode and the plate. The current that flows from the cathode to the plate passes right through the holes in the grid. If the vibrating current of a tank circuit is connected to the grid, the grid becomes alternately negative and positive, changing back and forth with the rhythm of the vibrations in the tank circuit. When the grid is negative, it tends to repel the electrons. This weakens the plate current. When the grid is positive, it helps the plate pull the electrons. This strengthens the plate current. As a result, the plate current vibrates in step with the vibrations in the tank circuit. If the plate current is fed into the tank circuit, it boosts the vibrations and keeps them from dying out. The current vibrating in the tank circuit is fed into an antenna from which the radio waves are broadcast into space.

TUNING IN A BROADCAST

Many stations send out radio broadcasts at the same time. The waves from all these stations strike the antenna of your radio receiver. But you don't hear these stations all at once. By merely turning a dial you choose the one station that you want to hear. To understand how it is possible to choose one out of many radio broadcasts, let us look again at the non-electrical vibrator, the pendulum. A boy on a swing is an example of a pendulum. The swing has a natural rhythm that depends on the length of the ropes supporting the swing. If the seat of the swing is given a push, the swing will move back and forth with that rhythm. If the seat is given a series of pushes, what happens depends on the rhythm of the pushes. If the pushes have a rhythm that is out of step with the rhythm of the swing, they interfere with the motion of the swing instead of helping it. Then the energy of the pushes is not passed on to the swing. But if the rhythm of the pushes is in step with the rhythm of the swing, they strengthen its motion, and make the swing ride back and forth in wide arcs. In this case the energy of the pushes is passed on to the swing. A radio receiver is like a swing that is being pushed. There is a tank circuit in the radio receiver, and the tank circuit has its own natural rhythm that depends on its inductance and capacitance. The tank circuit is being "pushed" by the radio waves that come to it from the broadcasting stations. Each set of waves has a definite rhythm which is the frequency of the waves. If the rhythm of the waves is not in step with the rhythm of the tank circuit, the waves do not pass any energy on to the receiver. If the rhythm of the waves is in step with the natural rhythm of the tank circuit, the waves do pass energy on to it, and build up a vibrating current in it. So the radio receiver picks up a broadcast only if the natural frequency of the tank circuit matches the frequency of the broadcast. But the frequency of the tank circuit can be changed. The dial on your radio is attached to the condenser in the tank circuit. When you turn the dial, you move the plates of the condenser and change its capacitance. In this way you change the natural frequency of the tank circuit. To tune in the broadcast you want to hear you give the tank circuit the frequency that matches the rhythm of the broadcast. Once the vibrations are started in the tank circuit, they are strengthened with the help of the radio tubes.

HOW RADIO WAVES CARRY SOUND

Sounds are made by vibrations with a frequency between 20 and 20,000 cycles per second. The radio waves in an AM radio broadcast have a frequency between 535,000 cycles per second and 1,605,000 cycles per second. Such high frequencies cannot make sounds that we can hear. In spite of that fact, radio broadcasts do bring us voices and the sound of musical instruments. This is done by using the high frequency radio waves as carriers, with low frequency vibrations riding on their backs. Then the low frequency vibrations are used to make the sounds we hear from the radio loud-speaker. Here is how radio waves in an AM broadcast are used to carry sound to our radio receivers. At the radio broadcasting station, first a tank circuit starts a vibrating current going. The rhythm of this cur-

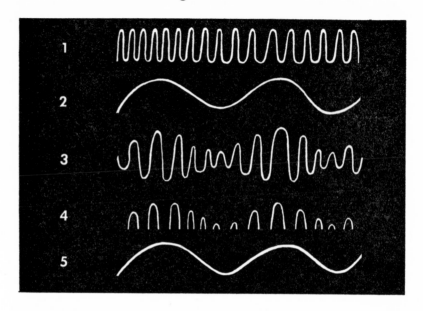

rent is shown in diagram number 1. Meanwhile the sounds of the radio program are picked up by a microphone. The microphone converts the sound signals into a vibrating electrical current, with a rhythm like that shown in diagram number 2. With the help of radio tubes, the two vibrations are combined, to form a more complicated rhythm like that shown in diagram number 3. Here we see the tank circuit rhythm carrying the sound rhythm on its back.

When a radio receiver tunes in this radio broadcast, a current begins to vibrate in the receiver with a rhythm like that shown in diagram 3. This is the combined rhythm of the high frequency radio waves and the low frequency vibrations that can be used to make sounds. These rhythms have to be separated if we want to hear the sounds. This is accomplished in several steps. First, with the help of a radio tube, the lower half of the wave is cut off, to produce the rhythm shown in diagram 4. Then, with the help of coils and condensers, the gaps in this wave are filled in. The result is a current vibrating with a rhythm like that shown in diagram 5. The rhythm is in step with the rhythm of the sound shown in diagram 2. When this current is used to produce vibrations in the loud-speaker, we get a copy of the sounds that were fed into the microphone at the radio station.

6

X RAYS

Electromagnetic waves with a frequency between 75,000 million megacycles and 4 million million megacycles are known as X rays. The first man-made X rays were produced by Wilhelm K. Roentgen in 1895. Because the frequency of X rays is so high, each X-ray photon has a tremendous amount of energy packed into it. As a result, X rays are *hard* and *penetrating,* that is, they can crash through thick layers of material that would stop the softer rays of lower frequency and longer wavelength.

TRANSMITTER FOR X RAYS

The transmitters that broadcast X rays are heavy atoms. A heavy atom has many electrons surrounding its nucleus, and the electrons are arranged in shells. We saw on page 38, that when an electron in the outermost shell is pushed to a higher energy level, and then falls back, it radiates visible light or u.v. light.

To get X rays out of an atom, it is necessary to displace one of the electrons in an *inner* shell. This can be done by bombarding the atoms with fast moving particles. If one of the particles penetrates through the outer shells and makes a direct hit on an electron in an inner shell, it may knock it out of the atom altogether, leaving a hole in the inner shell. Then an electron from one of the outer shells will fall in to fill the hole. Because it falls to such a low level, the electron releases a large amount of energy.

The photon that contains this energy then has a high frequency, and is an X-ray photon.

THE X-RAY TUBE

An X-ray tube is a device for bombarding heavy atoms to make them radiate X rays. A typical X-ray tube is shown in the diagram below. It is a vacuum

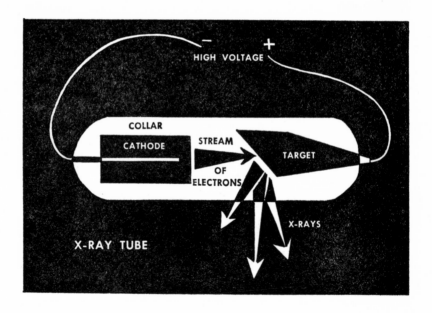

tube containing a tungsten wire cathode and a solid tungsten target. An electric current is passed through the cathode wire to make it hot. When the wire is hot, electrons leak off it into the tube. A high electrical voltage connected between the cathode and the target pushes the electrons toward the target. A metal collar around the cathode focuses the electrons into a narrow beam that strikes the target at high speed. The electrons smash into the inner shells of the atoms in the target, and then X rays are released, as described above.

X RAYS FROM THE SUN

There are X rays in the sunlight that enters the earth's atmosphere. But like the u.v. rays in sunlight, most of them never reach the ground. They are stopped by collisions with molecules high up in the air. These collisions knock electrons out of the molecules. The electrons and the broken molecules are charged particles known as *ions*. The region of the atmosphere where the ions are concentrated, more than fifty miles above the ground is known as the *ionosphere*. The bottom of the ionosphere behaves like a mirror for radio waves. When radio waves come up to it from the ground, they are reflected down again. This makes it possible to beam radio

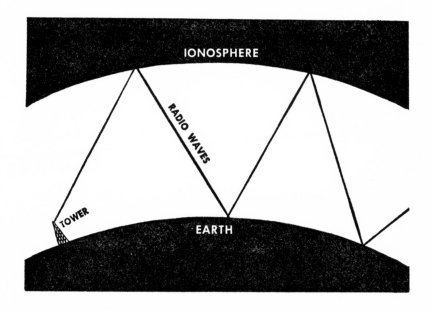

broadcasts around the earth by bouncing them off the ionosphere, as shown in the diagram.

X-RAY RECEIVERS

There are several different kinds of X-ray detectors or receivers in common use. One of them is ordinary photographic film. If a film that has been exposed to X rays is developed, it will show black deposits of silver particles just as if it had been exposed to visible light. For this reason, it is possible to take pictures with X rays.

Another type of X-ray detector is the ionization chamber, already described on page 62. A surge of current takes place through the chamber whenever a photon that enters the chamber succeeds in knocking electrons out of some atoms of the gas in it. It is possible to design the chamber so that it will respond to X-ray photons and to no others. This is done by using a filter in the window of the chamber, and by carefully choosing the gas in the chamber and the voltage that is applied to it. The filter keeps out of the chamber photons whose frequency is higher than that of X rays. So the only photons that enter the chamber are X-ray photons, or photons that have a lower frequency and therefore carry lower energy. The choice of gas and voltage guarantees that the gas atoms hold their electrons so tightly, that only the X-ray photons have enough energy to pry electrons loose. So, while the softer rays do enter the chamber, they are not detected. Ionization chambers have been put aboard rockets and earth satellites to detect the X rays in sunlight before they are blocked by collisions in the ionosphere.

A third type of X-ray detector is a screen made of a phosphor that fluoresces when it is struck by X rays. Such a screen is part of the fluoroscope used by doctors when they want to see the inside of your body.

SEEING THROUGH SOLIDS

Visible light cannot pass through the human body. But X rays are more penetrating, and can. When X rays are beamed through the human body, they pass through some parts of the body more easily than they pass through others. For example, they pass through flesh more easily than they pass through

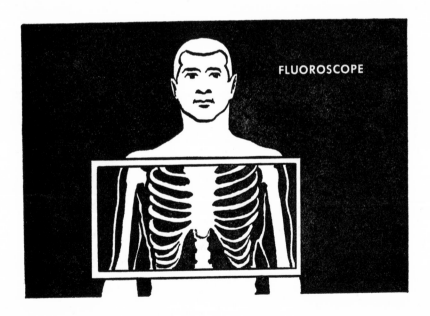

FLUOROSCOPE

bone. As a result, the bones cast a shadow. This shadow can be seen distinctly on the screen of a fluoroscope or on a photograph made with the X rays that have passed through the body. This fact makes it possible for doctors to look right through the body wall and see what is inside. When a doctor examines a patient with a fluoroscope, he places an X-ray tube behind the patient, and a fluorescent screen in front of him. X rays coming from the tube pass through the patient and make the fluorescent screen glow. Where the shadows of the bones and other dense parts of the body fall on the screen the glow is less bright. The pattern of dark and bright spots on the screen forms a picture of the interior of the body.

The penetrating power of X rays has made them useful to the machinery inspector and the art expert as well as to the doctor. Machinery inspectors can use them to "see" invisible flaws inside a machine. Art experts can use them to see what lies underneath a painting on a canvas. After World War II X-ray photographs helped to expose the art forgeries of the Dutch painter Van Meegeren. Van Meegeren was very skillful at imitating the style of painting of the old Dutch masters. He decided to make some paintings in this style, and claim that he "found" them in an attic, so that he could sell them at high prices as genuine old paintings done by famous painters. To be sure that his paintings looked old, he bought some old used canvases that already had paintings on them, and he painted right over them. However, X-ray photographs of his paintings foiled his plot. The X rays went right through Van Meegerens's paintings, so that the paintings beneath them showed up in the photographs. These hidden paintings were easily recognized by experts as paintings that were done *after the old masters died*. This proved that the paintings on top of them were not done by the old masters, so they were forgeries.

GRATINGS FOR X RAYS

A diffraction grating can bend rays of light only if the distance between adjacent lines on the grating is about the same length as a wavelength of the light. An X-ray wavelength is so small that there are from 300 million to 600 million of them in an inch. It is impossible to *make* a grating with lines that close. But we find some that are ready made in nature. Crystals are made up of closely packed layers of atoms. The distance between layers is so small that the layers of atoms do to X rays what the scratches on a grating do to visible light. So crystals can serve as gratings for bending X rays.

The way in which a crystal grating affects a thin beam of X rays is shown in the drawing below. The dotted lines represent two adjacent layers of atoms in the crystal. The ray marked AB strikes the upper

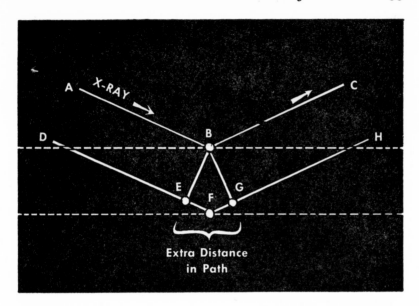

layer and is reflected along the path BC. The ray marked DF strikes the lower layer and is reflected along the path FH. The path DFH is longer than the path ABC by an amount equal to the length EFG. If this length contains a whole number of wavelengths, the rays BC and FH come out of the crystal in step and reinforce each other, so they combine to form a strong beam of light. If the length EFG does not contain a whole number of wavelengths, the rays BC and FH come out of the crystal out of step. Then they interfere with each other, so that no beam of light comes out in their direction at all. As a result beams come out only if they enter at certain special angles that depend on the wavelength of the rays and the distance between layers of atoms. If the distance between layers is known, then the angle of a beam that is reflected is a clue to the wavelength of the light. The calculations can also be made in reverse. If the wavelength of the X rays is known, then the angle of a beam that is reflected is a clue to the distance between the layers of atoms. Because of this fact, it is possible to figure out the structure of a crystal from the way in which it bends X rays. Different kinds of crystals bend X rays in different ways. The bent rays are used to make a photograph

X-RAY DIFFRACTION
PATTERN OF A DIAMOND

called an X-ray diffraction pattern. Crystals can be identified by the appearance of their X-ray diffraction patterns. The photograph above is an X-ray diffraction pattern made by a diamond crystal.

7

GAMMA RAYS

In 1896, the French physicist, Henri Becquerel, found that a photographic film placed by chance in a drawer overnight with a piece of uranium ore became fogged. This led to the discovery that uranium is *radioactive,* that is, that it sends out rays all by itself. Within a few years it was found that radium and thorium are also radioactive elements. Since then, many other radioactive elements have been found. Some exist in nature. Others are man-made products that result from smashing atoms in the laboratory.

If a sample of radium is placed in a lead dish with a narrow opening, the rays released by the radium come out of the opening in a narrow beam. If a magnetic field is placed across the beam, the beam splits into three rays. At first, when the nature of these rays was unknown, they were called alpha, beta, and gamma rays. (Alpha, beta and gamma are the first three letters of the Greek alphabet.) The way in which the beam splits is shown in the diagram below. If the direction of the magnetic field is at right angles to the page, the alpha rays curve upwards. The beta rays curve downwards, while the gamma rays move straight ahead without being affected by the magnetic field at all. The fact that the alpha and beta rays can be deflected by a magnetic field shows that they are made up of charged particles. They turn in opposite directions because

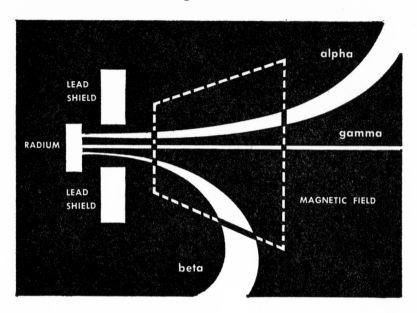

they have opposite charges. We know now that the
alpha particles are positively charged helium nuclei,
and the beta particles are negatively charged electrons. We know, too, that the gamma rays are not
deflected because they are electrically neutral. They
are electromagnetic waves that behave very much
like X rays except that they are more penetrating
than X rays are.

Gamma rays are electromagnetic waves with the shortest known wavelengths. The shortest gamma ray waves are so short, there are about one hundred thousand million of them in an inch.

EXPLODING ATOMS

These rays are released by radioactive elements when some of their atoms explode. The explosion occurs in the nuclei of the exploding atoms. The nuclei are broken into pieces, and lose some energy at the same time. The smaller pieces, the alpha and beta particles, are fired out of the nuclei at high speed. Part of the lost energy is fired out, too, in the form of gamma ray photons. A uranium nucleus breaks up in a series of thirteen explosions. After the fifth explosion, the part of the shattered nucleus that remains is a radium nucleus. After eight more explosions, this radium nucleus is changed into lead.

The atoms of a radioactive element do not all explode at once. In a pile of these atoms, only a certain fraction of them will explode in a second. Then, of those atoms that are left, the same fraction will explode in the next second. The rate at which the explosions take place, is given by the *half life* of the element. This is the length of time that it takes for half of the atoms in a sample of the element to explode. The half life of uranium is five billion years. The half life of radium is 1,600 years.

GAMMA RAYS FROM THE AIR

There is a small shower of gamma rays constantly falling on the ground from the air. These originate in the outermost layers of the atmosphere over a hundred miles above the ground. Here some of the atoms in the air are hit by fast-moving particles called cosmic rays that crash into the atmosphere from outer space. The collisions smash some of the atoms, releasing gamma rays from their breaking nuclei.

RECEIVERS FOR GAMMA RAYS

Gamma rays, like X rays and u.v. light, can be detected in an ionization chamber, where they open up a pathway for an electric current by knocking electrons out of atoms. The *Geiger tube* is a well known example of an ionization chamber. It is usually connected to an electrical counting device which counts the number of photons that enter the tube by counting the pulses of electric current that they cause.

Another device for detecting gamma rays is the *scintillation counter*, which combines a phosphor with a photomultiplier tube. When a gamma ray photon strikes the phosphor, it causes a flash of light. The light is picked up by the photomultiplier tube, where it causes an avalanche of electrons to flow in a pulse of current.

LUMINOUS WATCH DIALS

You have probably seen a watch or clock whose dial and hands glow in the dark. Gamma rays from exploding radium atoms are responsible for this glow. The face and hands of the clock were painted with a special paint containing a small amount of radium mixed with zinc sulphide, which is a phosphor. Some of the radium atoms are exploding all the time, and release gamma rays. Then the gamma rays strike the phosphor and make it glow.

RADIOACTIVE TRACERS

Atomic energy is produced by smashing atoms. Some of the fragments of the broken atoms are radioactive elements. Many of these radioactive elements are very useful as radioactive tracers. If a chemical element takes part in a complicated series of chemical changes, it is often difficult to know exactly what happens at each step in the series, and what part the element plays in each step. But if the element is radioactive, the job of tracing the steps in the process is made easier. Wherever the radioactive element goes, it fires out rays, and these rays can be detected. Radioactive carbon is now being used to try to solve the mystery of how plants convert carbon dioxide into sugar. The plants are fed carbon dioxide that contains radioactive carbon. As a result of chemical changes inside the plant, the radioactive carbon enters into first one compound and then another. By following the carbon from compound to compound, information is obtained about how sugar molecules are built inside the plant.

CANCER KILLER

The gamma rays released by radioactive elements are very useful for treating the disease known as cancer. A cancer is a growth made of body cells that have gone wild. If the cancer cells cannot be removed, they have to be killed. It is possible to kill them by exposing them to a radioactive element like radium. The hard, penetrating rays released by the radium smash into the cancer cells and destroy them.

RADIATION DAMAGE

Gamma rays are not particular about what kind of cells they hit. They can kill or damage healthy cells as well as cancer cells. So, whenever radiation is used, it has to be used with the greatest of care. Exposure to too much radiation can cause burns and serious illness. It is even possible for radiation to cause a cancer by damaging healthy cells and converting them into cancer cells. Hard X rays can also do damage if they are carelessly used. To protect the people, like physicists and doctors, who must work with radiation, equipment that produces radiation is shielded with thick layers of lead to cut off stray rays before they do any harm.

A special problem about radiation damage has been created by the testing of atomic bombs. The explosion of atomic bombs has put radioactive elements into the air. This has increased the amount of radiation that reaches the ground. The natural radiation caused by cosmic rays is responsible for making some people sick. The extra radiation caused by atomic bomb tests increases the amount of radiation sickness. To remove this danger, the governments that make atomic bombs are discussing plans to end explosions that put radioactive material into the air.

8

MICROWAVES

THE SMALLEST RADIO WAVES

Microwaves are the smallest radio waves. In the spectrum of electromagnetic waves they lie between infrared rays and the long radio waves described in Chapter 5. The shortest microwaves have a wavelength of about three hundredths of a centimeter and a frequency of one million megacycles. The longest microwaves have a wavelength of about three meters and a frequency of one hundred megacycles. The first microwaves made by man were the two-foot waves produced by Heinrich Hertz. The waves used most often in modern short wave equipment range from two feet down to a quarter of an inch in wavelength.

NEEDED FOR RADAR

Although Hertz used microwaves in his experiment, the scientists and inventors who followed him concentrated on the use of long waves for radio broadcasting. They switched to the long waves because they were easier to produce and send out over long distances. However, they had to return to the use of short waves in order to solve a problem that came up during World War II. The problem was, "How can you detect an approaching enemy plane while it is still far away?" A possible answer to the problem was to send out a beam of radio waves. If the beam struck an approaching plane, it would bounce back and be picked up by a receiver. The method could work, provided that it was possible to send out a narrow beam of radio waves that would travel in a straight line. Long radio waves could not be used for this purpose because they fan out too quickly from the broadcasting antenna. Very short waves were necessary to make the radar system work. So new transmitters and receivers were designed to make and use microwaves.

A NEW TANK CIRCUIT

To produce a steady stream of radio waves, it is necessary to have a vibrating electric current in a tank circuit (see page 76). The frequency of the waves depends on the inductance of the coil and the capacitance of the condenser used in the circuit. To make the frequency as high as possible, it is necessary to make the inductance and capacitance as low as possible. The inductance of a coil can be reduced by using fewer and fewer turns of wire in the coil. The smallest number of turns that can be used is *one*. The capacitance of a condenser can be reduced by reducing the size of the plates in the condenser. A very small capacitance is obtained, if instead of using a separate condenser, the opposite sides of a single turn of wire serve as the plates. So a single C-shaped turn of wire combines within itself the inductance and capacitance needed to produce a

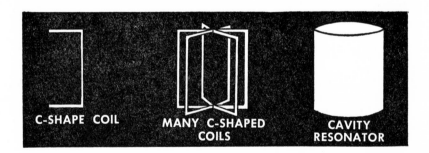

C-SHAPE COIL   MANY C-SHAPED COILS   CAVITY RESONATOR

high frequency wave. If many C-shaped loops are joined together in a circuit, as shown in the drawing, the inductance becomes smaller, but the capacitance increases. The effect is that the circuit produces the same frequency as a single loop of wire. But it has the added advantage of having a lower resistance. If so many loops are placed side by side that the spaces between them are completely filled, a cylinder is obtained, called a *cavity resonator*. It is the typical tank circuit for microwave transmitters and receivers.

NEW TUBES

Microwave broadcasting also needs new kinds of tubes. In an ordinary radio tube, electrons flow from the cathode to the plate. Although the distance between the cathode and the plate is short, it takes time for the electrons to cross this distance. If the grid of the tube is part of a circuit in which the electrical vibrations have a low frequency the time it takes the electrons to cross from cathode to plate is small compared to one cycle of the vibrations, so changes in the electron flow can easily keep step with the vibrations in the grid. But if the frequency is high, the time it takes the electrons to cross to the plate is large compared to one cycle of the vibrations. Then the flow of electrons quickly gets out of step with the vibrations in the grid and interferes with them. To avoid this difficulty, it is necessary to make tubes for high frequency radios very small. The tiny tubes that are used look like acorns and are known as *acorn tubes.*

For waves with a wavelength shorter than 1½ meters, vacuum tubes cannot be used at all. For these very short waves special tubes of an entirely new design are needed. One of the new kinds of tubes is known as a *magnetron.* Like an ordinary radio tube, it has a cathode and a plate. The plate is a metal cylinder lying between the poles of a magnet. The cathode is a wire in the center of the cylinder. A voltage is applied between the hot cathode and the plate. If there were no magnet present, electrons, leaking off the cathode, would flow in straight lines to the plate. A weak magnetic field makes the electrons veer and follow a curved path. A strong magnetic field curves the path so much that the electrons turn back before reaching

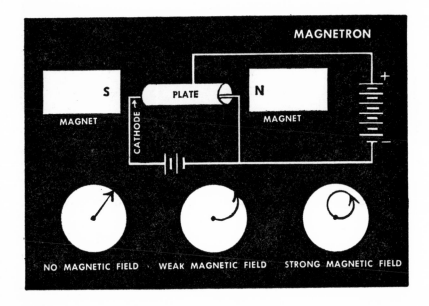

MAGNETRON

NO MAGNETIC FIELD · WEAK MAGNETIC FIELD · STRONG MAGNETIC FIELD the plate, and flow in circles instead. The circular flow causes electrical vibrations in the plate, and these are passed on to a tank circuit.

Another one of the new tubes is the *klystron.* The main parts of a klystron are an *electron gun,* a

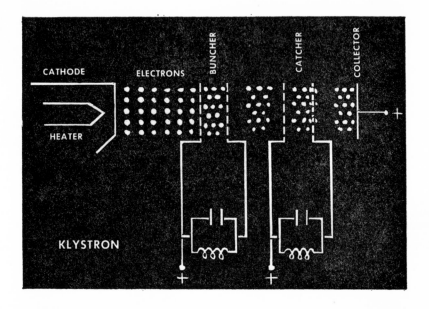

buncher, and a *catcher.* The electron gun consists of a cathode, a heater to make it hot so that electrons will leak off it, and a voltage to pull the electrons away from the cathode in a steady stream. The buncher is a pair of grids placed in the path of the stream of electrons. The grids are connected to a tank circuit, so they have a vibrating electric current in them. The electrical vibrations make the electrons in the stream bunch up as they pass between the grids. The catcher is a second set of grids placed past the buncher. When the bunched electrons flow through the catcher they cause electrical vibrations in the catcher. These vibrations can be used to strengthen the original vibrations in the tank circuit.

PIPES INSTEAD OF WIRES

In ordinary long wave radio, electric current is carried from one part of a circuit to another by a wire. When two wires lie side by side, there is a magnetic field and an electrical field in the space between them. As the current flows through the wire, an electromagnetic wave moves through the space between the wires. The wires serve to guide the motion of the wave, so we may think of them as *wave guides*. Because of the shorter wavelengths of microwaves, microwave equipment uses a different kind of wave guide. It uses pipes instead of

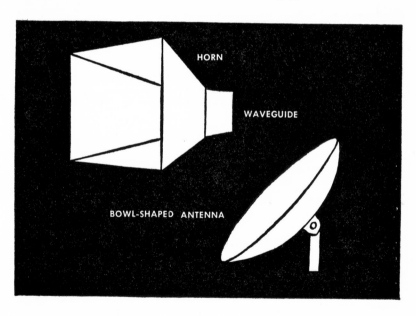

wires. The diameter of the pipe has to be about the same size as the wavelength of the wave that is being guided. At the end of the pipe it may flare out like a horn. The horn-shaped end of a wave guide serves as a radiator, sending out a directed beam of microwaves just as a megaphone sends out a directed beam of sound waves.

Microwaves may be broadcast either directly from the horn-shaped end of a wave guide, or from a bowl-shaped antenna. The waves are piped into the bowl, and the bowl acts as a reflector, sending the waves out in a directed beam in the same way that a search-light reflector sends out a beam of light.

USES OF RADAR

At Army posts guarding the borders of the United States, radar eyes constantly scan the sky, on the lookout for approaching planes. The eye is a combination microwave transmitter and receiver. The transmitter generates ultra-high-frequency radio waves, and a bowl-shaped antenna sends them out in pulses in a narrow beam. Meanwhile, the antenna rotates, so that each pulse goes out in a different direction. A pulse that strikes an object in the air bounces back and is picked up by the receiver, which records it as a spot on a screen like the screen of a television tube.

There are also many civilian uses of radar. It is used at airports, for example, to help control the flow of traffic. When visible light is completely blocked by a fog, the longer microwaves penetrate the fog easily. Then, although the men in the control tower cannot see the landing field by looking directly at it, they can see it by looking at its picture on the radar screen. Ocean-going steamers are now equipped with radar, too, so that they may see through a fog.

Radar has given the astronomer a way of making accurate observations of *meteors*. Meteors are chunks of metal or stone that fall into the earth's atmosphere from interplanetary space. They travel through the air so fast that they become very hot and burn up with a bright flash of light. The streak of light that they make across the sky is commonly called a "shooting star." As a meteor burns, it leaves a trail of smoke and gas behind. By bouncing radar pulses against the meteor trail, astronomers can now measure the height of the meteor, its speed, and the direction from which it came.

When a radar pulse is bounced against a distant object, the time it takes for the pulse to go out and back is a clue to the distance of the object. The radar pulse travels at the speed of light, which is about 186,000 miles per second. If the pulse returns three seconds after it was sent out, the total distance it traveled out and back is about 558,000 miles. Then the one way distance is about 279,000 miles. By bouncing radar pulses against the face of the moon, astronomers have made accurate measurements of the distance to the moon, which is about 240,000 miles.

RADIO ASTRONOMY

In 1932, Karl Jansky, an American telephone engineer who was searching for the causes of static in telephone lines, found that there are microwaves coming to the earth from outer space. This discovery was the beginning of the new science of *radio astronomy.* Now, while some astronomers continue to study the planets, the stars, and the space between the stars by the light that comes from them, other astronomers study them by means of the high frequency radio waves that come from them. They use specially built antennas of microwave receivers as radio telescopes. Some of them are bowl-shaped, like the antennas of radar installations.

A large part of the microwave radiation that comes to us from space originates in hydrogen atoms that are scattered in the space between the stars. Each hydrogen atom is like a small radio transmitter. There is a single electron revolving around the nucleus of the atom. This electron spins like a top. Sometimes the electron flips over as it spins, and sends out a microwave photon with a frequency of 1,420 megacycles, and a wavelength of 21 centimeters. By receiving these hydrogen broadcasts, astronomers get information about how much hydrogen there is in space, and how it moves. By tuning in on the hydrogen in the great dust clouds of the Milky Way, they found that the Milky Way has spiral arms and is spinning like a giant pinwheel.

There are some parts of the sky from which strong steady radio signals are received. These are known as *radio stars*. While some of the radio stars are simply stars sending out radio waves, others are not stars at all. One of the radio stars, for example, is the Crab Nebula, which looks like an irregular patch of cloud when it is viewed through a telescope. The Crab

CRAB NEBULA

Nebula is what is left of a star that exploded in the year 1054. Another interesting radio star, known as Cygnus A, consists of two galaxies that are colliding.

(A galaxy is a giant family of billions of stars.) Although we see this collision now, it really happened 270 million years ago. The galaxies are so far away, it took the light and the microwaves 270 million years to get here and tell us about the collision.

EFFECT ON ANIMALS

Microwaves focussed on a living body can influence its behavior. Part of the effect is caused by heat. But there is another part caused in some other way. This fact was proved in some recent experiments performed in the United States, England, and Canada. To eliminate the heating effect of the microwaves, the experimenters sent out the waves in pulses. Each pulse, as it fell on the body it was aimed at, warmed it up slightly. But, between pulses, the heat had a chance to flow away. So there was no accumulation of heat, and the temperature of the body remained practically steady. In one series of experiments, the pulses were focussed on one-celled animals swimming in water. By changing the frequency of the microwaves, it was possible to control the direction in which the tiny animals swam. In another experiment, the microwaves were focussed on the brains of some monkeys. Although there was no noticeable heating effect, the waves interfered with the functioning of the monkeys' brains. In some cases the monkeys died in a few minutes. Scientists hope that through more of these experiments they can find out why microwaves have these mysterious effects. When they are better understood, microwaves may turn out to be useful in medicine for curing infections, or for treating nervous disorders.

9

MESSENGER OF
THE UNIVERSE

All material bodies are made of electrical particles. As they move, and whirl, and spin, they send out
electromagnetic waves. These waves reach us from
all parts of the universe. They come to us from atoms
that are too small to be seen. They come to us from
stars and giant systems of stars that are great distances away. Hidden within the waves we find information about the bodies that they come from.
The electromagnetic waves are messengers of the

universe, bringing us messages that scientists have learned how to read and interpret.

MESSAGES FROM THE ATOMS

An atom radiates electromagnetic waves when one of its electrons falls from a higher to a lower energy level. By measuring the frequency of the radiated waves, physicists have obtained information about the levels at which the electrons may be found. They have counted the electrons that surround the nucleus, discovered that they are arranged in layers or shells, and have measured the distance from the nucleus to each shell. Nearly all the information we have about the structure of the atom has come from studying the light or the u.v. rays or the X rays that atoms radiate.

AN ATOM'S FINGERPRINTS

There are about one hundred different kinds of atoms. Each one is like a radio station capable of broadcasting electromagnetic waves. Different atoms broadcast waves of different frequencies, so, like a radio station, an atom can be recognized by the frequency of the waves it broadcasts. If a chemical element is evaporated to form a gas, and the gas is made to glow by heating it, or passing an electrical spark through it, the color of the glow, which depends on the frequency of the waves sent out by the atoms in the gas, is a clue to what kind of atoms they are. For example, atoms of the metal sodium usually glow with a yellow light. You can see this yellow light by sprinkling some table salt over a gas flame. There is sodium in the table salt. The heat of the flame separates some of the sodium atoms out of the salt and makes them glow. Atoms of the gas neon glow with a red light. Long glass tubes filled with neon are bent into various shapes to make the neon signs that you see on store fronts and billboards.

When a gas made of many atoms of one kind is made to glow, the atoms don't all broadcast the same color of light. Each atom is capable of broadcasting many frequencies. While one atom broadcasts one frequency, its neighbor may broadcast another. If the light received from the gas is passed through a slit to form a thin beam, and then is passed through a prism or a diffraction grating to form a spectrum, the spectrum appears as a series of lines separated by blank spaces. Each line represents one of the frequencies radiated by some of the atoms. The set of lines is like a fingerprint of the atom. People can be recognized by the lines in their fingerprints, because no two people have the same prints. In the same way, atoms can be recognized by the lines in their spectra, because no two kinds of atoms have the same spectrum.

MESSAGES FROM THE STARS

When we look at the night sky, we see it covered with the dots of light we call stars. The light from any one star is a faint trickle. Astronomers carefully gather this light and concentrate it with the help of lenses or curved mirrors in their telescopes. Then they measure the light in various ways. They measure the direction from which it comes. They measure the intensity of the light. They spread the light out in a spectrum and measure the frequency of each color that appears. Each of these measurements is a clue which they can interpret with the help of physical theory and mathematics. From these clues they find out how far away a star is, how fast it moves, how big it is, how heavy it is, how hot it is, and what it is made of.

The chief clue to the distance of a star is the intensity of its light, because the further away a star is the fainter it looks. The chief clue to the temperature of a star is its color. The cooler stars are red hot, while the hotter stars are white hot. More detailed clues to temperature are found in the spectrum of a star. The spectrum also gives information about the chemical composition of the star, because each chemical element on the surface of the star puts its fingerprint on the light of the star. Light coming from the hot, glowing center of the star contains all colors. When the light passes through the cooler outer layers of gas in the star, the atoms absorb some of the light. Each atom withdraws from the light certain special colors. The missing colors show up as dark lines in the spectrum of the star. These are the fingerprints by which the atoms can be identified.

TOP SPEED

Electromagnetic waves are the fastest things that move. The speed of light through empty space is about 186,000 miles per second. According to modern physical theory, no material body can ever move as fast. By using powerful magnets, we can push an electron until its speed is close to the speed of light. But we cannot get it to reach the speed of light, because the faster it moves, the heavier it gets, and the heavier it is, the harder it becomes to make it move faster.

The speed of light was measured for the first time in the seventeenth century by the Danish astronomer Olaus Römer. Römer had studied the moons of Jupiter, and knew the rhythms with which they revolved around it. From these rhythms he could predict when a moon would be eclipsed by passing behind Jupiter where we could not see it. But then

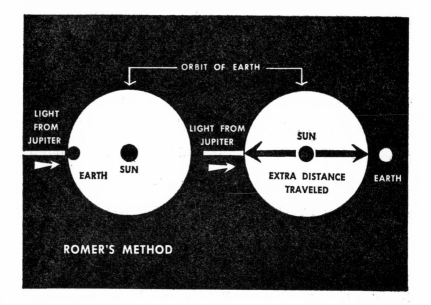

ROMER'S METHOD

he found that some of the eclipses were late. Suppose that the eclipses we saw when the earth and Jupiter were on the same side of the sun were on time. Then the eclipses that were seen six months later, when the earth was on the other side of the sun, turned out to be one thousand seconds late. Römer realized that we saw these eclipses later because the light from Jupiter had to travel a greater distance to reach us then. The extra distance traveled by the light was the width of the earth's orbit, which is 186,000,000 miles. Since the light covered this distance in 1,000 seconds, he found the speed of light in miles per second by dividing 186,000,000 by 1,000.

ENERGY FROM MATTER

It used to be thought that matter could not be destroyed, but could only be rearranged. Now physicists have discovered that particles of matter *can* be destroyed. But when they are destroyed, photons of electromagnetic radiation are created to take their place. For example, electrons can be destroyed. An electron has a negative charge. There is another particle called a positron, which resembles an electron except that it has a positive charge. When an electron and positron meet, they destroy each other, and a photon of electromagnetic radiation arises to take their place. The amount of energy formed depends on the amount of mass that is destroyed. Mass is converted into energy according to a fixed rule: to find the amount of energy that is formed, multiply the amount of mass destroyed by the speed of light and then again by the speed of light. Since the speed of light is a very large number, a small amount of mass can be converted into a large amount of energy. In an atomic bomb, electrons are not destroyed, but something similar takes place. Part of the *mass* of the bomb is converted into energy. That is why this kind of bomb produces tremendous amounts of energy.

The conversion of matter into energy is reversible. Under certain special conditions, a photon can split into a positron and an electron. Then the energy of the photon disappears, and electrical particles of matter takes its place. This shows that electromagnetic radiation has a very special place in the universe. Besides being the messenger of the universe, it is the raw material out of which all other things are made.

INDEX

A NOTE ON THE

TYPE

IN WHICH THIS BOOK IS SET

THE TEXT of this book is set in Caledonia, a Linotype face designed by W. A. DWIGGINS. It belongs to the family of printing types called "modern face" by printers—a term used to mark the change in style of type-letters that occurred about 1800. Caledonia borders on the general design of Scotch Modern, but is more freely drawn than that letter.

THE BOOK was composed, printed, and bound by H. Wolff, New York. PAPER made by P. H. Glatfelter Co., Spring Grove, Pa. TYPOGRAPHY by Tere LoPrete.